Puzzle 1

Travel Quiz
a game for two players

What are the capital cities of the following countries?

1. Spain

2. England

3. Greece

4. Germany

5. Sweden

6. Denmark

7. America

8. Russia

9. Italy

Puzzle 2

All the fun of the fair

Can you spot ten differences between these two pictures?

Puzzle 3

Which vegetable for dinner?

Use the pictures to solve the crossword.

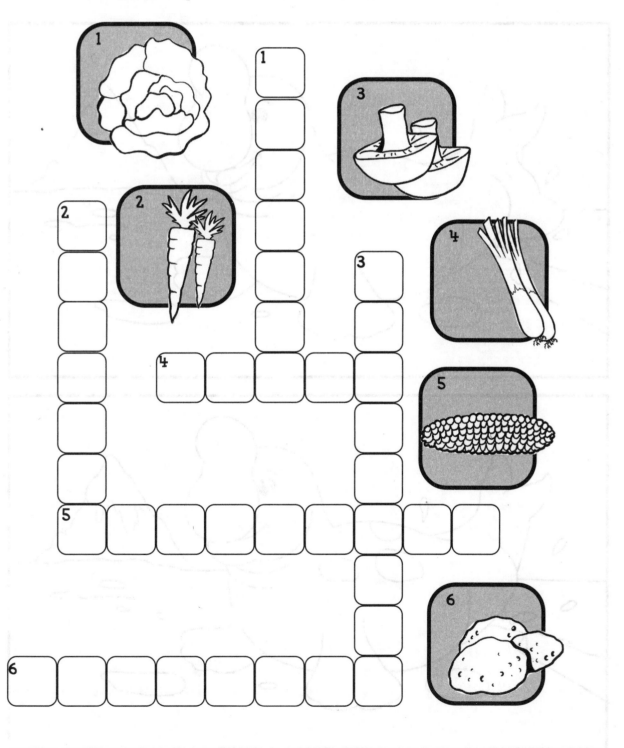

Puzzle 4

Water time fun

Can you spot five differences between these two pictures?

Puzzle 5

Use the alphabet code below to work out what these crabs mean. Write your answer at the bottom.

a b c d e f g h i j k l m
1 2 3 4 5 6 7 8 9 10 11 12 13

n o p q r s t u v w x y z
14 15 16 17 18 19 20 21 22 23 24 25 26

- - - - -

Puzzle 6

Time for housework

Can you spot ten differences between these two pictures?

Puzzle 7

CROSSWORD!

Work out the words for these pictures and then complete the crossword below.

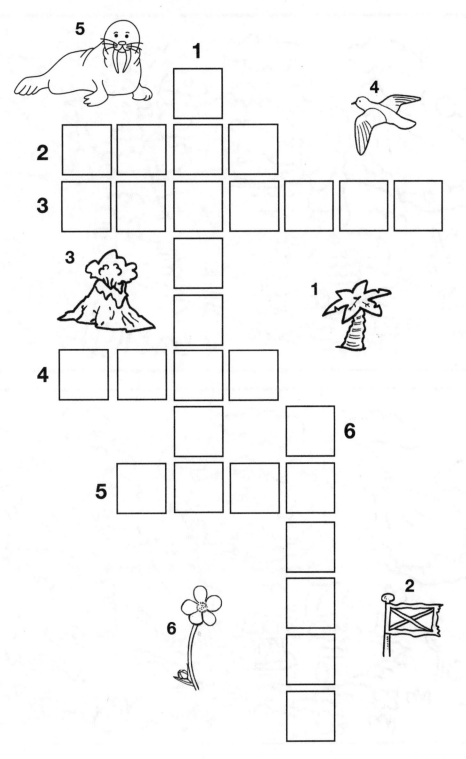

Puzzle 8
Picnic in the country

Can you spot ten differences between these two pictures?

Puzzle 9

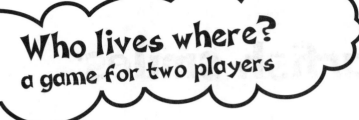

Who lives where?
a game for two players

Draw a line to match each person to a famous place in their country.

Puzzle 10

Starfish smiles

Can you spot five differences between these two pictures?

Puzzle 11

Travel Quiz
a game for two players

Unscramble these words to discover the names of cities in the United Kingdom.

1. **abht**

2. **cnatrebruy**

3. **drmhau**

4. **slisbryau**

5. **stloirb**

6. **chstree**

7. **xfrdoo**

8. **wnichsetre**

9. **wrocsetre**

Puzzle 12

Time for a rest

Can you spot five differences between these two pictures?

Puzzle 13

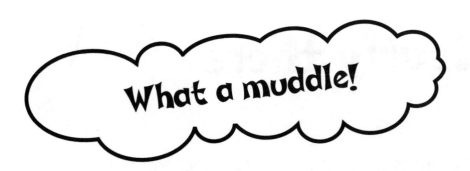

What a muddle!

The names of some items you may take on holiday have been muddled up. Using the pictures, can you work out what they are?

MREACA

SLGSASENUS

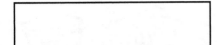

TAEUSISC

NURACOBLIS

Puzzle 14

Nearly there

Can you spot ten differences between these two pictures?

Puzzle 15

Can you find the six dinosaur names
hidden in this wordsearch?

Maiasaura   Barosaurus
Apatosaurus   Triceratops
Pachycephalosaurus Albertosaurus

P	F	Q	D	B	M	A	I	A	S	A	U	R	A	A	G	T	C
D	A	H	Y	P	A	C	H	O	J	A	U	T	U	L	L	R	O
S	L	C	E	R	Y	R	K	O	L	E	W	A	R	J	X	I	E
L	I	P	H	F	A	W	O	T	Z	D	Y	G	Y	E	W	C	L
Y	N	V	S	Y	L	C	I	S	C	L	F	G	T	A	B	E	O
R	H	G	K	A	C	S	W	C	A	K	Z	N	H	L	H	R	N
J	A	E	Y	F	U	E	K	E	U	U	V	S	O	Q	K	A	H
N	C	D	R	H	J	R	P	R	W	J	R	C	S	W	N	T	Y
S	C	F	T	E	L	L	O	H	A	M	R	U	S	C	C	O	S
O	A	L	B	E	R	T	O	S	A	U	R	U	S	A	K	P	L
J	C	Q	E	T	Z	H	N	O	E	L	A	F	R	C	T	S	S
A	G	L	H	W	S	Q	X	P	Y	L	O	A	U	B	M	R	I
G	D	H	K	A	Z	I	O	S	B	G	T	S	S	L	R	C	S
R	S	M	N	E	R	Z	J	A	C	F	H	A	A	Q	J	R	C
A	P	A	T	O	S	A	U	R	U	S	K	R	U	U	K	E	H
S	L	U	B	I	T	O	C	A	B	R	U	K	A	Q	R	R	L
C	G	K	R	W	H	Y	E	C	J	P	W	I	G	S	O	U	A
P	U	O	D	L	O	C	X	P	K	A	G	U	S	C	H	S	S

Puzzle 16

Yo-yoing

Can you spot ten differences between these two pictures?

Puzzle 17

Days of long ago!

Use the pictures to solve the crossword.

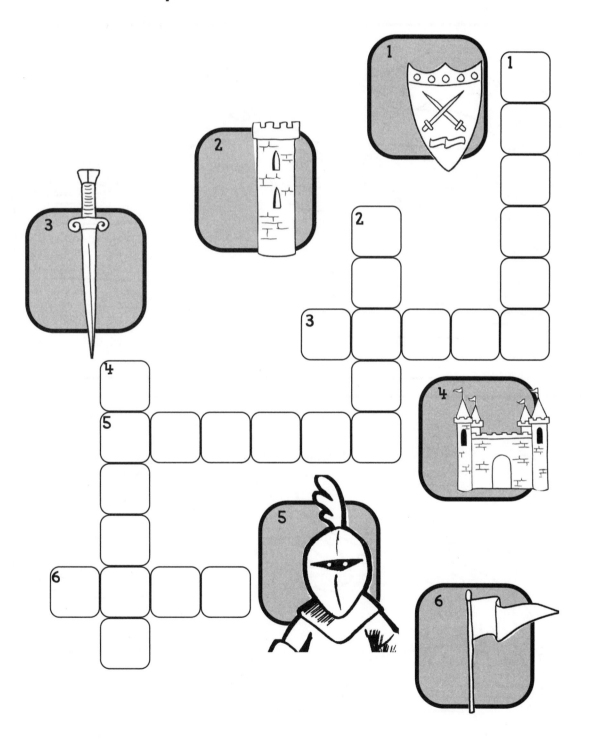

Puzzle 18

Waiting for friends

Can you spot three differences between these two pictures?

Puzzle 19

What do you like doing?

Use the pictures to solve the crossword.

Puzzle 20

Monkeying around

Can you spot ten differences between these two pictures?

Puzzle 21

Baby Animals
a game for two players

Do you know the terms for babies
of the following animals?

1. Cat

2. Dog

3. Fox

4. Cow

5. Pig

6. Sheep

7. Duck

8. Hen

9. Peacock

Puzzle 22

Swimming along together

Can you spot five differences between these two pictures?

Puzzle 23

Can you see these in your garden?

Use the pictures to solve the crossword.

Puzzle 24

Slothing around

Can you spot five differences between these two pictures?

Puzzle 25

How many words can you make from the word butterflies?

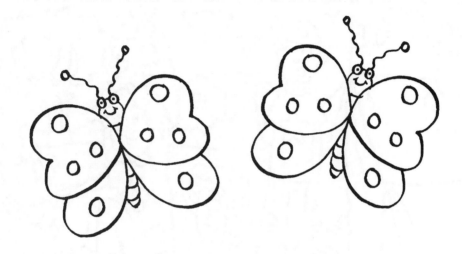

BUTTERFLIES

_____   _____

_____   _____

_____   _____

_____   _____

_____   _____

_____   _____

Puzzle 26

We love the outdoor life

Can you spot ten differences between these two pictures?

Puzzle 27

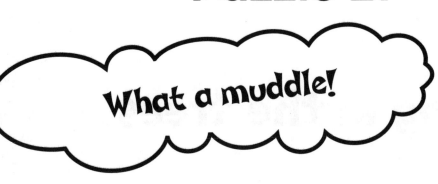

What a muddle!

The names of famous cities have been muddled up. Using the pictures, can you work out what they are?

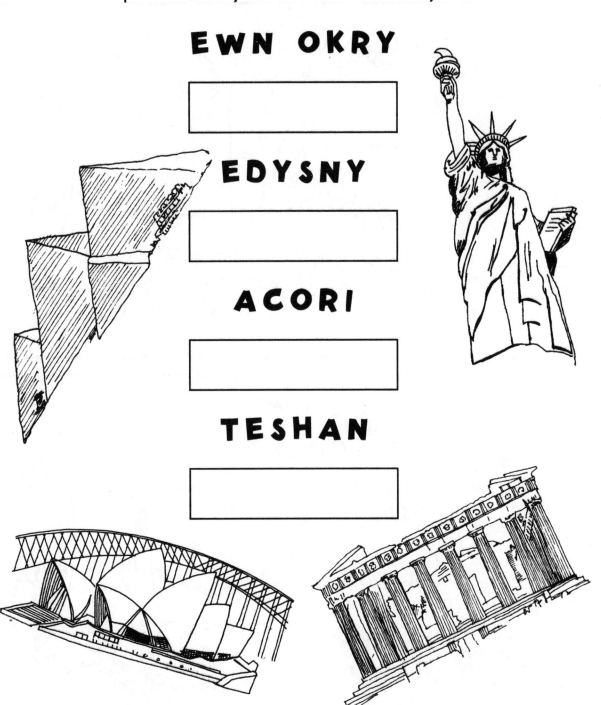

EWN OKRY

EDYSNY

ACORI

TESHAN

Puzzle 28

Hiding in the trees

Can you spot five differences between these two pictures?

Puzzle 29

CROSSWORD!

Use the pictures to solve the crossword.

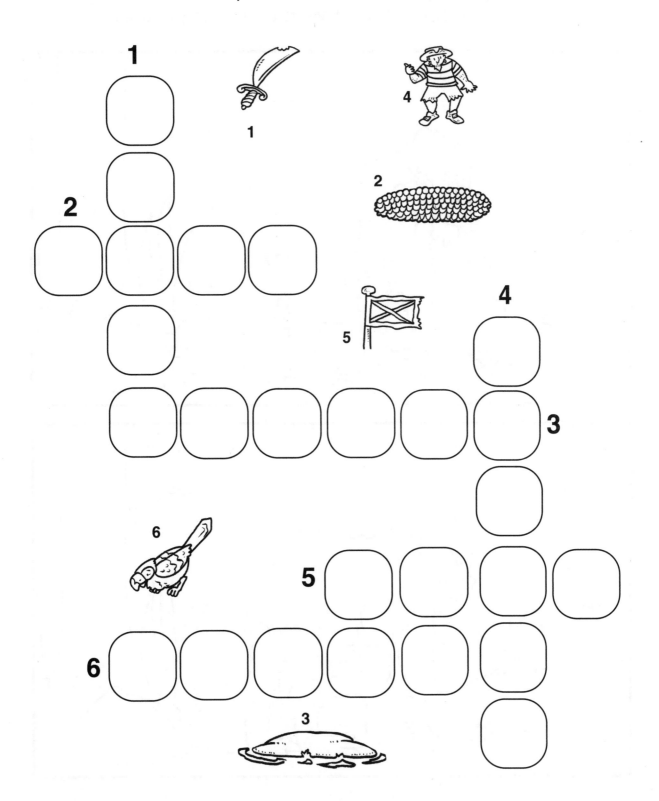

Puzzle 30

All alone

Can you spot four differences between these two pictures?

Puzzle 31

Cheesy search!

Find some different types of cheese in the grid below.

BRIE   **EDAM**
CHEDDAR   **GOUDA**
CHESHIRE   **GRUYERE**
CREAM   **LEICESTER**
FETA   **STILTON**

U	R	U	N	A	Y	R	C	A	Z	C
P	E	T	J	G	A	F	M	Q	P	V
H	T	G	Z	R	T	E	F	I	R	D
C	S	O	Z	U	E	R	W	P	V	R
H	E	U	T	Y	F	I	G	E	A	E
E	C	D	C	E	E	H	X	D	N	M
Q	I	A	A	R	N	S	D	R	A	L
I	E	R	F	E	S	E	J	E	E	V
P	L	B	B	Q	H	H	R	E	D	M
P	L	M	A	C	R	C	Z	N	A	Z
N	O	T	L	I	T	S	G	S	M	M

Puzzle 32

Stingray surprise

Can you spot five differences between these two pictures?

Puzzle 33

Flora and fauna quiz

Use the pictures to solve the crossword.

Puzzle 34

Shiver me timbers

Can you spot ten differences between these two pictures?

Puzzle 35

How many words can you make from the word elephant?

ELEPHANT

_____ _____

_____ _____

_____ _____

_____ _____

_____ _____

_____ _____

Puzzle 36

We're hungry

Can you spot ten differences between these two pictures?

Puzzle 37

Sports Quiz
a game for two players

Unscramble these words to discover names of sports.

1. mnibdatno

2. ootfabll

3. bllaent

4. hckyoe

5. rgbyu

6. ccrikte

7. ordersun

8. letcsitha

9. nniset

Puzzle 38

Howzat

Can you spot ten differences between these two pictures?

Puzzle 39

It's magic!

Use the pictures to solve the crossword.

Puzzle 40

The truth is out there

Can you spot ten differences between these two pictures?

Puzzle 41

CROSSWORD!

Use the pictures to solve the crossword.

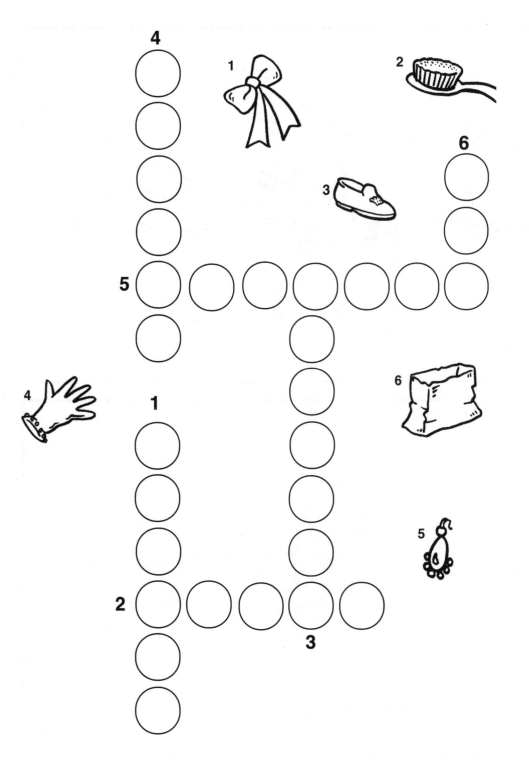

Puzzle 42

Waiting around

Can you spot five differences between these two pictures?

Puzzle 43

Can you find these words in this under the sea wordsearch?

angelfish

waves

bubbles

crab

dogfish

catfish

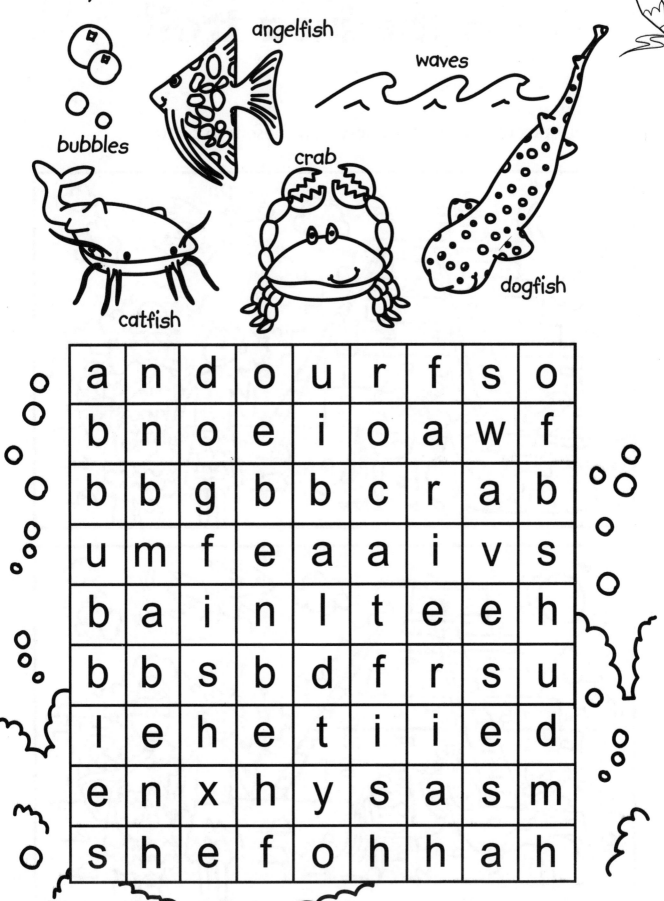

a	n	d	o	u	r	f	s	o
n	n	o	e	i	o	a	w	f
b	b	g	b	b	c	r	a	b
u	m	f	e	a	a	i	v	s
b	a	i	n	l	t	e	e	h
b	b	s	b	d	f	r	s	u
l	e	h	e	t	i	i	e	d
e	n	x	h	y	s	a	s	m
s	h	e	f	o	h	h	a	h

Puzzle 44

On the Inca trail

Can you spot ten differences between these two pictures?

Puzzle 45

Wordsearch
a game for two players

Find some ball games in the grid below.

BOWLS   POOL
CRICKET   RUGBY
CROQUET   SKITTLES
GOLF   SQUASH
POLO   TENNIS

H	I	B	W	K	Y	O	S	F	Q	H
B	E	E	K	B	I	E	C	W	R	L
O	C	K	G	T	L	R	I	S	O	O
W	B	U	U	T	O	I	I	O	J	U
L	R	D	T	Q	L	G	P	Z	O	L
S	T	I	U	E	H	S	A	U	Q	S
Q	K	E	O	Z	K	I	N	I	V	M
S	T	F	N	G	Q	C	O	L	M	N
O	L	X	O	N	C	T	I	L	E	L
D	E	L	D	A	I	A	M	R	O	A
Y	F	A	S	Z	U	S	Q	N	C	P

Puzzle 46

Cat on the move

Can you spot six differences between these two pictures?

Puzzle 47

Bath time!

Use the pictures to solve the crossword.

Puzzle 48

All the way to the top

Can you spot ten differences between these two pictures?

Puzzle 49

Circular wordsearch
a game for two players

Can you find six famous deserts hidden in the grid below?
Look at the clues around the edge.

MOJAVE

GOBI

SYRIAN

ARABIAN

SAHARA

KALAHARI

N P L X G O B I D
N A G N U K L A
S A R A S S Y R I A N R G O
A H A A A B M
H A C S R A B I E M P A K D
S A S A R O M P A K A L
J I D L A R D R E M A R M A V
R R P O M N A O
A Z M D P A J
M D P A H
K L A H
L N E V A
N E V

Puzzle 50

Up on the mountain

Can you spot five differences between these two pictures?

Puzzle 51

You'll find these on a farm!

Use the pictures to solve the crossword.

Puzzle 52

Splashing about

Can you spot ten differences between these two pictures?

Puzzle 53

Wordsearch

Find some noises your pets may make in the grid below.

BAA   NEIGH
BARK   PURR
CHIRP   SNARL
GROWL   SQUEAK
MIAOW

I	J	H	H	P	P	V	F	T	X	Y
R	B	I	O	C	K	Z	X	L	T	X
R	N	A	M	R	H	N	U	Q	V	Z
U	S	T	A	W	E	I	B	S	T	S
P	O	B	O	I	U	S	R	B	R	S
A	B	A	G	S	S	W	S	P	Q	G
T	I	H	R	E	X	N	J	U	O	A
M	B	E	O	W	A	L	E	H	X	V
Q	Z	X	W	R	J	A	U	T	P	P
A	K	C	L	Y	K	K	U	N	D	H
T	N	L	K	Q	O	U	Z	X	J	O

Puzzle 54

Shark surprise

Can you spot five differences between these two pictures?

Puzzle 55

Delicious fruit!

Use the pictures to solve the crossword.

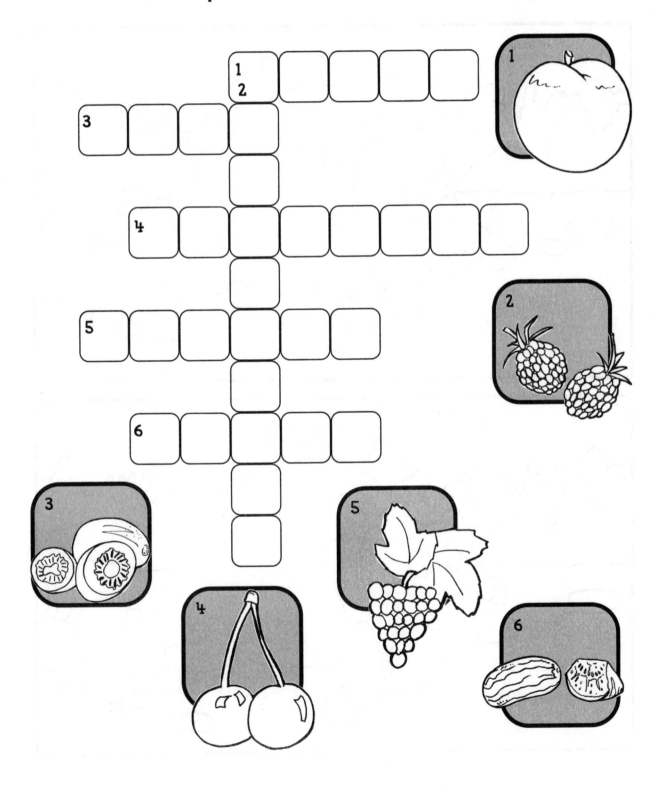

Puzzle 56

Boar on the run

Can you spot six differences between these two pictures?

Puzzle 57

Write down the first letter of each object in
the wheel to spell the hidden name of this
dinosaur who had a huge dome on the top
of its head, which was made of solid bone.
The arrow shows the object name with the
first letter of the dinosaur.

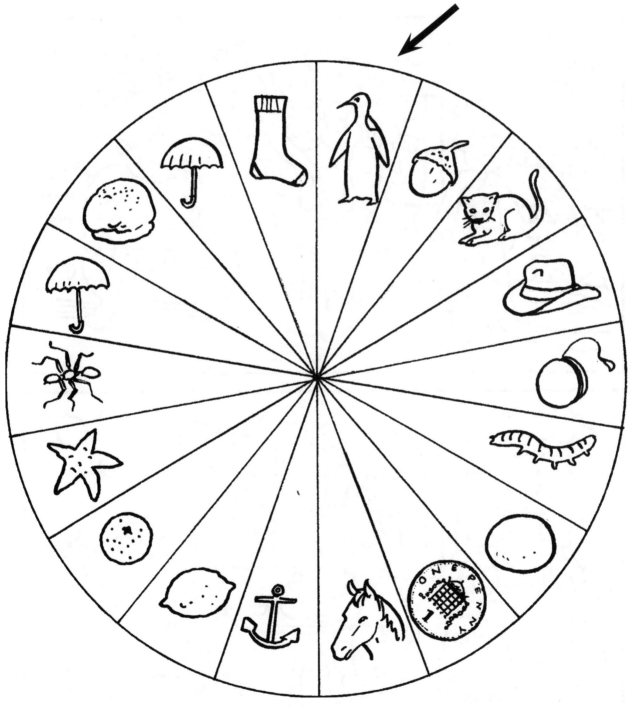

Puzzle 58

The house of the rising sun

Can you spot ten differences between these two pictures?

Puzzle 59

Nature search!

Use the pictures to solve the crossword.

Puzzle 60

Yummy, Barbecue time

Can you spot ten differences between these two pictures?

Puzzle 61

Job Quiz
a game for two players

Can you guess these people's jobs?

1. I steer a ship.

2. I work in a school.

3. I work in Space.

4. I fly an aeroplane.

5. I look after people who are ill.

6. I look after animals who are ill.

7. I look after people when they are swimming in the sea.

8. I cook food.

9. I milk cows.

Puzzle 62

Breathe in

Can you spot ten differences between these two pictures?

Puzzle 63

High flyers!

Use the pictures to solve the crossword.

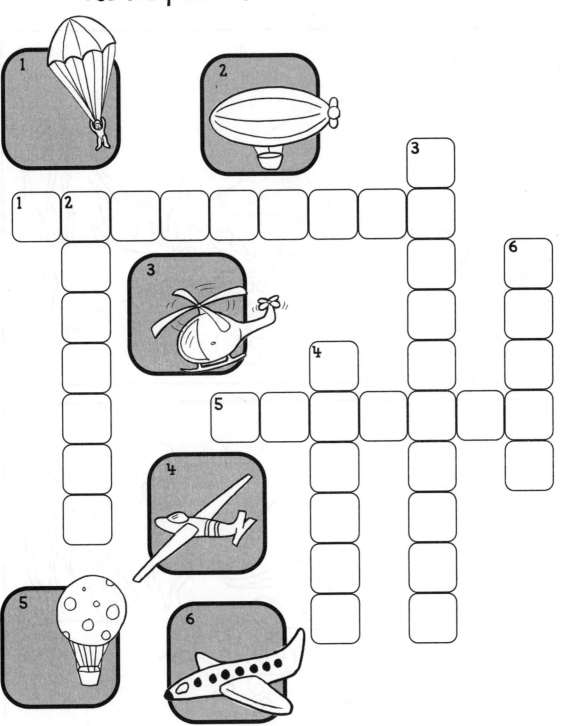

Puzzle 64

Dolphin and friends

Can you spot six differences between these two pictures?

Puzzle 65

Join the boxes
a game for two players

You will need two players for this game. Take it in turns to draw over the dotted lines. You are only allowed to draw over one side of a box per go. The person who closes off a box puts their initial in that box. The person with the most number of initials at the end is the winner!

Puzzle 66

Scoot, scoot, scooter

Can you spot ten differences between these two pictures?

Puzzle 67

Muddled up!

The names of these countries and continents have been muddled up.
Can you work out what they are?

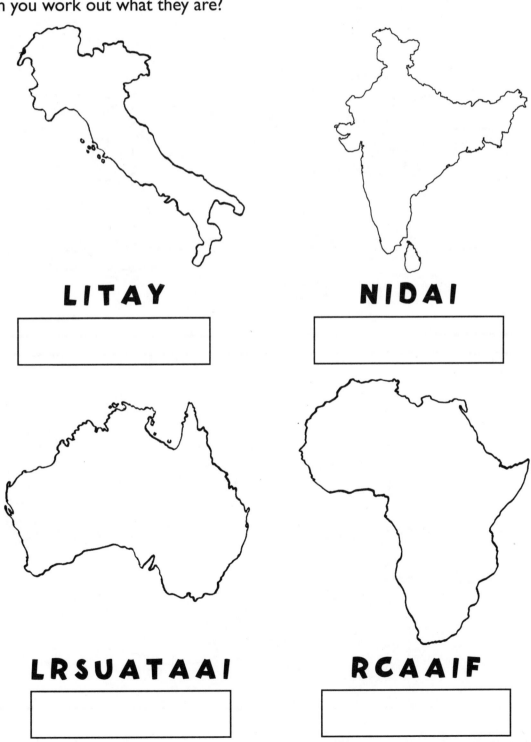

LITAY

NIDAI

LRSUATAAI

RCAAIF

Puzzle 68

Seal island

Can you spot five differences between these two pictures?

Puzzle 69

Can you find these fish words in the wordsearch?

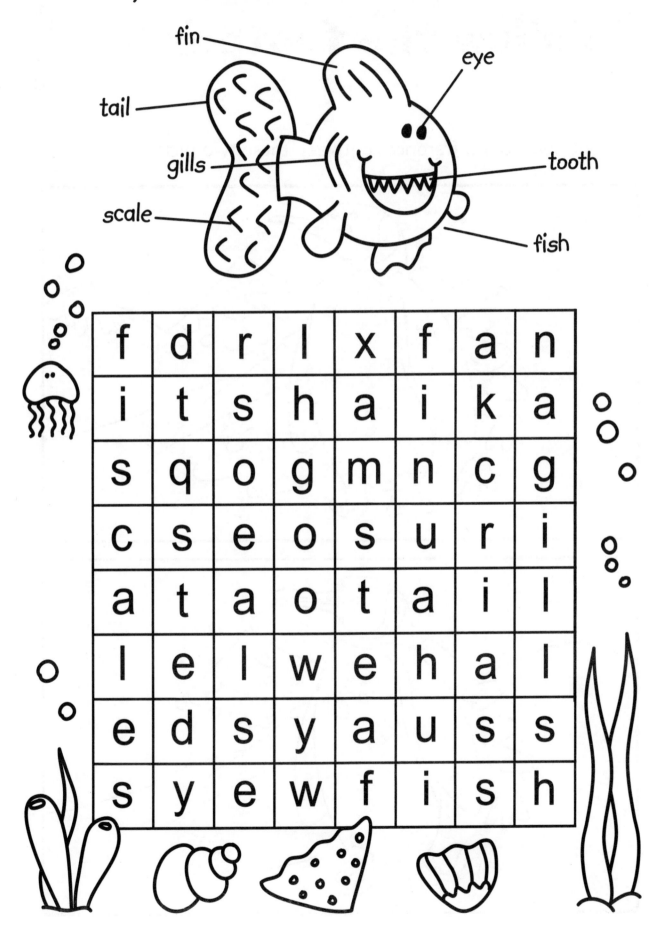

fin, eye, tail, gills, tooth, scale, fish

f	d	r	l	x	f	a	n
i	t	s	h	a	i	k	a
s	q	o	g	m	n	c	g
c	s	e	o	s	u	r	i
a	t	a	o	t	a	i	l
l	e	l	w	e	h	a	l
e	d	s	y	a	u	s	s
s	y	e	w	f	i	s	h

Puzzle 70

Follow the footprints

Can you spot four differences between these two pictures?

Answers

Answers

PUZZLE 1

1. Madrid   2. London

3. Athens   4. Berlin

5. Stockholm   6. Copenhgen

7. Washington   8. Moscow

9. Rome

PUZZLE 2

PUZZLE 3

1. Lettuce

2. Carrots

3. Mushrooms

4. Leeks

5. Sweetcorn

6. Potatoes

PUZZLE 4

PUZZLE 5

Claws

PUZZLE 6

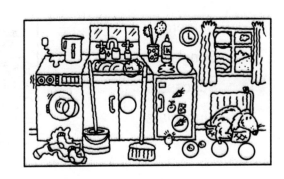

PUZZLE 7

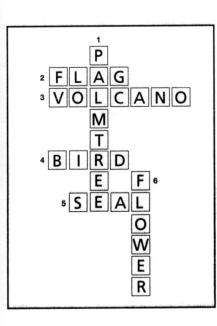

PUZZLE 8

PUZZLE 9

Answers

PUZZLE 10

PUZZLE 11

1. Bath	2. Canterbury
3. Durham	4. Salisbury
5. Bristol	6. Chester
7. Oxford	8. Winchester
9. Worcester	

PUZZLE 12

PUZZLE 13

Camera

Sunglasses

Suitcase

Binoculars

PUZZLE 14

PUZZLE 15

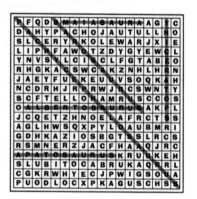

PUZZLE 16

PUZZLE 17

1. Shield

2. Tower

3. Sword

4. Castle

5. Armour

6. Flag

PUZZLE 18

Answers

PUZZLE 19

1. Sleeping
2. Swimming
3. Sailing
4. Jumping
5. Running
6. Riding

PUZZLE 20

PUZZLE 21

1. Kitten   2. Puppy
3. Cub   4. Calf
5. Piglet   6. Lamb
7. Duckling   8. Chick
9. Peachick

PUZZLE 22

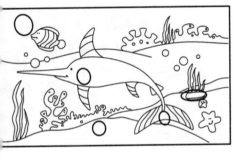

PUZZLE 23

1. Poppy
2. Buttercup
3. Thistle
4. Roses
5. Honeysuckle
6. Leaves

PUZZLE 24

PUZZLE 26

PUZZLE 27

New York
Sydney
Cairo
Athens

PUZZLE 28

Answers

PUZZLE 29

1. Sword
2. Corn
3. Island
4. Pirate
5. Flag
6. Parrot

PUZZLE 30

PUZZLE 31

PUZZLE 32

PUZZLE 33

1. Worms
2. Garden
3. Hedgehog
4. Birds
5. Frogs
6. Snails

PUZZLE 34

PUZZLE 36

PUZZLE 37

1. Badminton
2. Football
3. Netball
4. Hockey
5. Rugby
6. Cricket
7. Rounders
8. Athletics
9. Tennis

PUZZLE 38

Answers

PUZZLE 39

1. Doves
2. Cloak
3. Magician
4. Cards
5. Rabbit
6. Hat

PUZZLE 40

PUZZLE 41

1. Ribbon
2. Brush
3. Slipper
4. Gloves
5. Earring
6. Bag

PUZZLE 42

PUZZLE 43

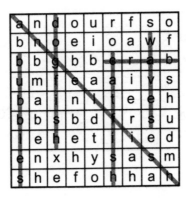

PUZZLE 44

PUZZLE 45

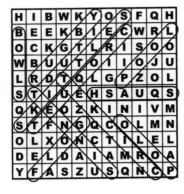

PUZZLE 46

PUZZLE 47

1. Baths
2. Soap
3. Tap
4. Towel
5. Shower
6. Sink

Answers

PUZZLE 48

PUZZLE 49

PUZZLE 50

PUZZLE 51

1. Goat
2. Geese
3. Tractor
4. Cat
5. Donkey
6. Hens

PUZZLE 52

PUZZLE 53

PUZZLE 54

PUZZLE 55

1. Peach
2. Pineapples
3. Kiwi
4. Cherries
5. Grapes
6. Melon

PUZZLE 56

Answers

PUZZLE 57

Pachycephalosaurus

PUZZLE 58

PUZZLE 59

1. Bat
2. Woodpecker
3. Stoat
4. Badger
5. Beaver
6. Pigeon

PUZZLE 60

PUZZLE 61

1. Captain
2. Teacher
3. Astronaut
4. Pilot
5. Doctor
6. Vet
7. Life guard
8. Chef
9. Farmer

PUZZLE 62

PUZZLE 63

1. Parachute
2. Airship
3. Helicopter
4. Glider
5. Balloon
6. Plane

PUZZLE 64

PUZZLE 66

Answers

PUZZLE 67

ITALY   INDIA

AUSTRALIA   AFRICA

PUZZLE 68

PUZZLE 69

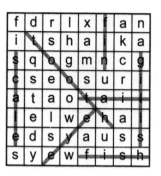

PUZZLE 70